Blue John
Stone

BRADWELL
BOOKS

Published by Bradwell Books

11 Orgreave Close Sheffield S13 9NP

books@bradwellbooks.co.uk

All rights reserved. No part of this publication may be reproduced, stored in a retrieval system or transmitted in any form or by any means, electronic, mechanical, photocopying, recording or otherwise without the prior permission of Bradwell Books.

British Library Cataloguing in Publication Data: a catalogue record for this book is available from the British Library.

1st Edition

ISBN: 9781912060641

Text by: Vicky Turner & Gary Ridley

Edited by: Camilla Zajac

Design and typeset by: Mark Titterton

Image Credits: Mark Titterton, Karl Barton, Glen Segal and Andy Caffrey (p.28)

Print: Gomer Press, Llandysul, Ceredigion SA44 4JL

In Memory of Peter Harrison,
Cyril Adamson and Trevor Ford OBE

Acknowledgements

Thanks to Noel Worley, Graham and Lesley Ollerenshaw, Blue John Cavern and staff, Treak Cliff Cavern and staff, Blue John Gems Ltd, Peter Ashmore, Kay Harrison, Jean Adamson, Chris Gill, The Peveril Centre, Janet Baxter and the Ford Estate and Chatsworth House.

References

'Blue John Cavern and Mine' by Arthur E Ollerenshaw undated

'Treak Cliff Cavern and the Story of Blue John stone' by TD Ford and PC Harrison 1992

'Derbyshire Blue John' by TD Ford 2000

'Castleton Caves' by TD Ford 2008

'The Castleton Mines, A Descriptive and Visual History' by JH Reiuwerts and P Wolstenholm 2016

Unpublished writings and memoirs by PC Harrison

Front Cover: Underground in Treak Cliff Cavern

Back Cover: Treak Cliff Hill and (inset) a selection of Blue John objects **Page 1:** Blue John bell shaped vase

Contents

1. Introduction and brief geology   4

2. The colour of Blue John stone   6

3. The Veins of Blue John stone   8

4. Mining Blue John stone   12

5. The caverns today   14

6. Blue John stone look-a-likes   19

7. Blue John stone past and present   21

1. Introduction & brief geology

Of all the semi-precious minerals, Blue John stone is perhaps the most intriguing. It is a very rare form of a common mineral, fluorspar or fluorite, and is only found in one place in the world and that is Castleton in Derbyshire. The exact location of the only site for Blue John is a small hill called Treak Cliff, which lies a quarter of a mile west of Castleton in the Hope Valley of Derbyshire. Over several centuries, thousands of tonnes of Blue John stone have been mined from Treak Cliff Hill and scars from that mining can still be seen on the surface. Today, both Treak Cliff Cavern and Blue John Cavern are open to those visitors wanting to learn more about Blue John stone. Both caverns still contain veins of Blue John, although it is becoming much rarer. The Blue John Cavern is located on the North West of Treak Cliff Hill while the Treak Cliff Cavern is to be found on the eastern slope of Treak Cliff. While other mines are also located on Treak Cliff, they have long since been closed.

The home of Derbyshire Blue John, Treak Cliff Hill is mostly made of limestone which started to form 330 million years ago when the British Isles were much closer to the equator and Derbyshire was part of a shallow tropical lagoon. At around 240 million years ago, movements in the earth's crust caused some of the limestone to break, creating a sloping bed of massive boulders. The cracks between the boulders were filled with mineral-rich hot fluids and, as the fluids cooled, the minerals crystallised in layers. These minerals became fluorite, calcite, barite and galena. Over millions of years, the fluorite formed into what we now call Blue John stone.

First recorded in writing in the 17th century, Blue John became popular as an ornamental stone because of its beautiful colours and unique patterning. It was widely coveted by the rich as a stylish way to adorn their country houses and palaces. While the mineral's chemical name is calcium fluoride (formula CaF_2), its more evocative everyday name is something of a mystery. There are a number of theories about where the name "Blue John" comes from. One theory suggests that the name is a corrupted version of the French description of its colour, "bleu et jaune", which means "blue and yellow". However, there is no known evidence to verify this claim. The other theory is that lead miners gave the mineral its name after mistaking it for a zinc mineral called sphalerite, which they called Black Jack. Another twist on this theory is that the miners chose to call the mineral by a similar name out of choice rather than error. We'll probably never know the origins of the name, but there is no doubt that this mystery is very much part of Blue John's enduring appeal.

Treak Cliff Hill

2. The colour of Blue John stone

Blue John's pleasing colours are caused by the way that the light reacts with its crystals. The make-up of these crystals is quite a complex story…

Purple, blue and white

Blue John is a variety of the mineral calcium fluoride (CaF_2) and its crystals are naturally cube-shaped. These crystals are formed from fluorine and calcium atoms bonded together and ordered into a lattice shape. Scientific analysis of the crystals has identified minute particles of what is known as colloidal calcium trapped within the lattice. The colloidal calcium was formed by the disruption of the crystals during their formation. The most likely cause of this disruption was the low natural ionizing radiation coming from the limestone and shale rocks which surround the mineral veins of Treak Cliff and Castleton. The areas of highly concentrated radiation minerals at Treak Cliff match with the areas of Blue John deposits, making them very likely to be the cause of the striking purple colour. The difference in thickness and shade of the colour banding could be related to the variation in the amount of time that the layers have been exposed to radiation during the growth of the crystals.

The colloidal calcium in Blue John crystals absorbs all the colour wavelengths except blue and purple, so these are the colours we see when we look at Blue John in daylight. This is because white light is made up of a mixture of different colours or wavelengths which correspond to the colours seen in the rainbow spectrum. Colour is produced from white light when colours are selectively absorbed; if all are absorbed equally, a mineral appears to be white or colourless to the human eye.

Yellow and iridescence

Iron is another important aspect in the varied colours of Blue John. In Treak Cliff Hill, iron is produced through the weathering of the shales in the boulder bed. Water seeping through the soil dissolves some of the iron and finds its way into the cavern. The iron in the water becomes concentrated in two ways:

Through a chemical reaction which forms insoluble iron compounds that show up as the 'ochre' or yellow colour in Blue John

Natural anaerobic bacteria called Leptothrix concentrate the iron as part of their life processes and is often seen as oily layers (called biofilm) in badly drained land or ponds. This biofilm or iridescence sometimes coats the Blue John stone, especially near the boulder bed. Because of its basic blue or purple colour, the biofilm can appear as a coppery metallic sheen on the surface of the Blue John stone, even when dry.

ABOVE: Metallic effect on Blue John stone

TOP: Five Vein

3. The Veins of Blue John Stone

The diversity in Blue John's colour banding is incredible, especially when you consider that the stone only comes from one place in the world. The mineral fills old caves or the spaces between the boulders in the boulder bed. This kind of void lining is called a "pipe vein". There are fifteen separate named veins of Blue John, but

Variants of Millers Vein

many more variants or related patterns, thanks to the sheer variety of colours and styles. As miners followed a specific vein, the patterns and colours gradually changed as they progressed. A good example of this is the Millers Vein, while Old Tor Vein and Winnats One Vein can occur very close together with separate distinct patterns.

The following images are cross-sections of the fifteen named veins. They have been cut and polished to highlight the colours and patterns.

Lower Cliff Blue Vein

Upper Cliff Blue Vein

Winnats Five Vein

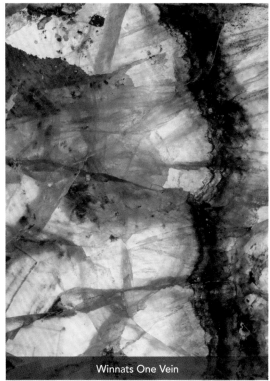

Winnats One Vein

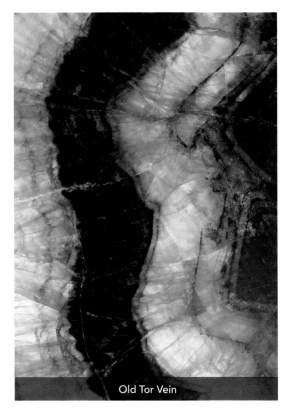

Old Tor Vein

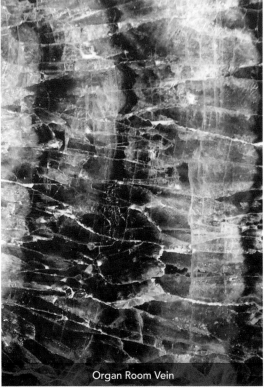

Organ Room Vein

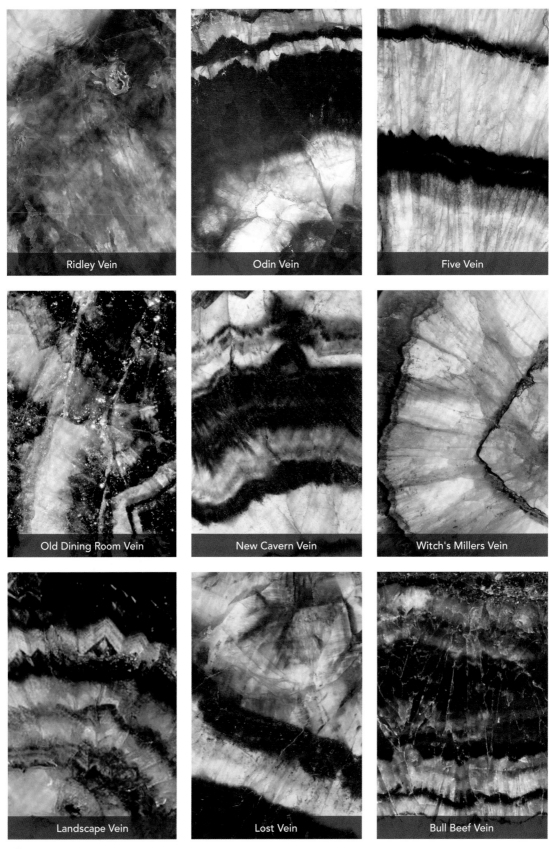

Ridley Vein

Odin Vein

Five Vein

Old Dining Room Vein

New Cavern Vein

Witch's Millers Vein

Landscape Vein

Lost Vein

Bull Beef Vein

New Dinning Room Vein Vein

Twelve Vein

Twelve Vein Bowl

There are also vein patterns for which the location is no longer known, such as Oxlow Vein and Windy Knoll Vein. Today, unless it is known where the Blue John was mined or unless the pattern and colour is very distinct, it can be difficult to identify the original vein name. This is particularly so with items of jewellery where the finished Blue John pieces are relatively small.

4. Mining Blue John stone

There is documented evidence that Blue John has been mined from Treak Cliff Hill for at least 300 years. Written records mention lead mining taking place before 1699 on the hillside; Blue John mining appears to have started after 1709. The Blue John stone in Treak Cliff Hill only occurs in small deposits which line the walls of the caverns or fill the cavities of pipe veins formed in limestone (as mentioned earlier, pipe veins are mineral veins which, as the name suggests, are long and narrow). Blue John also occurs as single nodules in deposits of clay, left behind by the water which created the caves. The nodules are highly prized for their beautiful colours arranged in concentric bands or layers.

Mining Blue John is a complex undertaking for many reasons. It must be carried out with extreme care to avoid damaging the precious mineral. Explosives are not used to break out the stone because it would cause fracturing and loss of colour, making it useless for further working. Methods of extraction usually involve the removal of any surrounding limestone to access the Blue John.

Millers Vein Nodule

While some mining methods have changed, others are very similar to the techniques of the past. In the old days, the traditional method of stitch drilling and "plug and feather" used a long drill bit (turned by hand) to bore a series of holes into the limestone surrounding the Blue John. Wooden pegs were then inserted into these holes and metal chisels or wedges hammered into the pegs. This caused the limestone to split, forming a line of fractures between each hole. As the limestone split and came away from the wall, pieces of intact Blue John could be removed. Another approach was to leave the wooden pegs in overnight, dampen them and let the resulting swelling of the wood do the work of splitting the rock.

Two more traditional methods were to push lime into the drill holes as this would swell and split the limestone, or workers would simply sift through the sediment found in the caves by hand or with spades.

These days, drilling and wedging is still used to extract Blue John. The holes are drilled into the limestone alongside the Blue John, with a heavy duty electric drill. Wooden plugs are pushed into the holes, and metal wedges/chisels hammered into the pegs to shatter the joint-blocks.

Alternatively, a stone cutting diamond tipped chainsaw is used. It is quieter and produces less vibration than a drill, causing even less damage to the stone. Now more regularly-shaped and larger blocks (up to 50 kilos) of Blue John can be cut out in a single piece. Once extracted, the Blue John goes to the workshop where it is washed and sorted for further processing for ornaments and jewellery or for geological specimens for research.

5. The caverns today

Every year, thousands of people head to Castleton and many choose to visit the caves. Access to the caves is on foot and by guided tour only. Due to the naturally steep contours of the hillside above and below ground, the caverns are not accessible to wheelchair-users. Inside the caves, there are steps and steep slopes, but the handrails and electric light throughout make visiting as comfortable as possible in this challenging environment. Visitors can take their time and will be well rewarded by the wonders of the caverns.

Blue John Cavern

The Blue John Cavern comprises a series of large soaring chambers which are now beautifully floodlit: they need to be seen to be believed. The Blue John Cavern is located towards the top of Treak Cliff Hill, opposite Mam Tor, and is approached by a short walk from the main road to the entrance. Once underground, the route for visitors is made up a series of steps cut into a natural pothole originally used for access by the old miners. This leads down to the Twelve Vein workings and a display of old mining

Blue John Cavern Entrance

Blue John Cavern

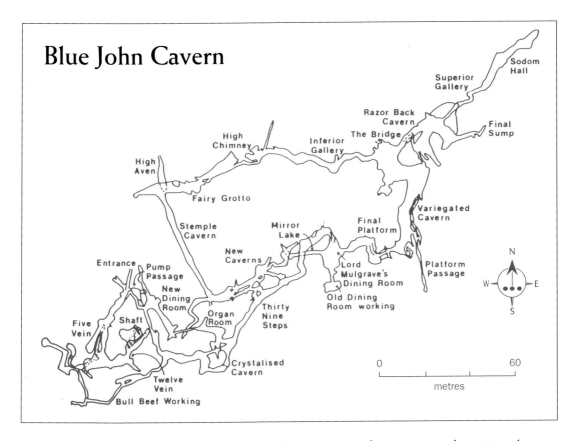

equipment. Energetic tourists were originally taken into the cavern in the 1770s down a rough ladder or rope, until the stairway was built in 1836. The Victorians and later visitors were taken around by candlelight: the Grand Crystallised Cavern was once illuminated by a chandelier of 28 candles, as described in a guidebook from 1846. Another fascinating cavern is Lord Mulgrave's Dining Room. Its distinctive round shape was created by two underground rivers which met to form a whirlpool. The cavern takes its name from Lord Mulgrave who is said to have hosted a dinner party for the miners in it!

Along this route are passages leading off into the different Blue John workings of Bull Beef and Landscape Veins concealed behind doors in the cavern walls, but these are not accessible to the public. It is possible to see a series of caves that were shaped by a river which dried up many years ago. There are also side passages that branch into the Organ Room Vein and the Old and New Dining Room workings. The workings

extend to the New Cavern Vein of Blue John, but the Dining Room Vein is the only vein visible to the public on the guided tour. The final chamber is the Variegated Cavern which leads to steps and the outside world.

Pillar of Blue John

Treak Cliff Cavern

Treak Cliff Cavern is situated on the northeast side of Treak Cliff Hill that faces the village of Castleton and is reached by steps and a path from the roadside below. This cavern was originally two Blue John stone mines. One was the Old Miller's Mine, which was worked from the early 1700s and which gave the Millers Vein its name. A little higher up was the Cliff Side Mine, where there are extensive workings in the Treak Cliff Blue Vein. At some time in the mid-1700s, the miners from each mine broke through into each other's workings. In 1926, miners broke through into a breathtaking series of stalactite 'Wonder' caves. In the early 1930s, work began to adapt the caves and workings for visitors by constructing paths and steps and fitting handrails and electric lights into the Miller's Mine, the Cliff Side Mine and new 'Wonder' caves. The mine and caves eventually opened to visitors as Treak Cliff Cavern in 1935.

Millers Vein Chalice

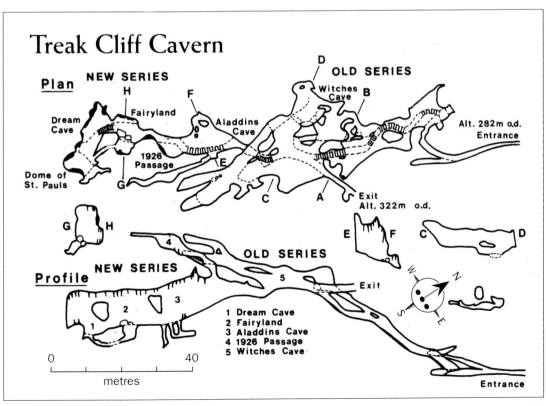

17

Ridley Vein in situ

The entrance to the cavern comprises a low narrow tunnel leading to the Lower Treak Cliff Blue Vein workings and the Ridley Vein which was newly discovered on the 15th November 2014 - the first discovery for 150 years! A passage which is inaccessible to visitors branches off the Fossil Cave to some of the Miller's Vein workings. The footpath rises steeply to the Witch's Cave where the Upper Treak Cliff Blue Vein and its associated workings are visible, including the Blue John Pillar. The route to the 'Wonder Caves' takes visitors downwards via a few steps into Aladdin's Cave, Fairyland, the Dream Cave and the Dome of St. Paul's. The Dream Cave has some of the finest stalactites in the Peak District. The guided tour for visitors ends here. Visitors exit the cave by retracing their steps to the Witch's Cave and to an exit higher up the hill. A short downhill walk leads to the Cavern Visitor Centre and museum adjacent to the cavern entrance.

Other workings on the hill include a location near the Odin Mine, a lead mine where the Odin Vein of Blue John was worked and an unknown location towards Windy Knoll for the Windy Knoll Vein. Along Winnat's Pass is the Old Tor Mine, presumed to be the location of Winnats One and Winnats Five Veins.

All the lead and Blue John workings both above and below ground have been designated as part of the Castleton Site of Special Scientific Interest (SSSI). Rock, fossil and mineral collecting is strictly prohibited, with fines and penalties enforced by Natural England. The mines and mineral rights to the Blue John stone are privately owned.

6. Blue John stone look-a-likes

Blue John has been popular for over 300 years and continues to be so today. Many pieces appear for sale and on auction internet sites. However, pieces described as Blue John may actually be Chinese Fluorite or Amethyst, both of which can bear a resemblance to the mineral. In the 1700s, adverts referred to Blue John as "Mock Amethyst". Mistakes are still made today - even in reputable auction sale rooms. Here are some of the signs that what you are looking at is genuine Blue John stone:

Amethyst   Chinese Fluorite   Chinese Fluorite

- Distinctive blue-purple and golden-yellow banding

- Occasional surface marks

- Signs of fluorescence on exposure to ultraviolet light
  (but this only applies to certain types and so is fairly rare).

Because each piece of the mineral is unique, it's not easy to be sure that you are looking at genuine Blue John. So, the best thing to do is to go to a reputable jeweller or to the Castleton caverns and shops and you'll know that you're buying the real thing!

7. Blue John stone past and present

The beauty of Blue John has been recognised for many years. Many surviving objects tell a fascinating story of how the world was charmed by the mineral's appeal. The earliest documented evidence for the decorative use of Blue John stone goes back as far as 1760. The architect Robert Adam designed and installed fireplace surrounds in Kedleston Hall near Derby, one of which featured Miller's Vein Blue John.

Dedicated craftsmen

Blue John's popularity grew even more in the late 18th century. Thanks to the expansion of the railways and improvements to roads, the late Georgians and Victorians travelled extensively. Tourism to Derbyshire flourished, and Blue John stone craftsmen made smaller items and souvenirs that were affordable and more easily transported, including small bowls, cutlery handles and jewellery of all kinds. Workshops established in Derby, Buxton, Bakewell, Matlock Bath and Castleton produced an impressive array of items. It was during this period that larger Blue John ornaments became most popular.

Here are just some of the people who worked with Blue John and made sure that its popularity endured…

Matthew Boulton

Mathew Boulton (1728 -1809), the famous Birmingham manufacturer, introduced the use of ormolu (gilded metal) fittings to decorate lathe-turned solid body shapes made of Blue John stone. In the late 18th century, he designed and made candelabra, urns, vases and perfume burners. Sadly, Boulton failed in his attempt to lease all the Blue John mines in 1768, but he did manage to buy 14 tonnes in 1769. As you might expect from this brilliant engineer and manufacturing innovator, Boulton is credited with developing new ways to use Blue John to make products. For while early pieces of Blue John were solid or shaped only on the outside, it is thought that Boulton was the person who introduced the use of pine resin to strengthen the mineral during shaping and polishing. This innovative method allowed the solid shapes to be hollowed out and the stone to be sawn or cut much thinner, making the objects translucent and revealing the natural beauty of the stone. If you're lucky enough to have a spare £50 note in your purse or wallet, you will find this Blue John innovator pictured on one side.

Solid ornament from Winnats One Vein

John Vallance

Records have generally not survived from the 18th and 19th centuries so Blue John pieces can only rarely be associated with particular craftsmen, or even accurately dated. Thankfully, some information has survived, giving us a vivid if somewhat fragmented picture of the popularity of Blue John during this period.

One of the names in Blue John for that period was John Vallance who opened what is today known as the Royal Museum in Matlock Bath, where he made and sold many Blue John items. He and his 'Derbyshire Spar' vases were listed in the catalogue of the 1851 Great Exhibition held in London.

Hollow vase, circa 1830, probably made by John Vallance. It was purchased from Mrs Smith of the Royal Museum in Matlock Bath in the mid 20th century

The Chatsworth Tazza has a diameter of approximately 60cm

© Devonshire Collection, Chatsworth.
Reproduced by permission of Chatsworth Settlement Trustees.

The Shore Vase in Chatsworth. As with most large hollow Blue John ornaments, this is built up in 'rings' of stone. The Shore Vase is unusual because each ring is made of three pieces carefully fitted together

© Devonshire Collection, Chatsworth. Reproduced by permission of Chatsworth Settlement Trustees.

Harry Grant & Sons

Another name closely associated with Blue John was that of the Watcombe Marble Works in Devon. This was established in 1836 and it continued through the ownership of the Grant family to become Harry Grant & Sons. Grant's made some very fine Blue John ornaments.

A selection of ornaments made by Harry Grant & Sons

The 20th Century

Fortunately, record keeping improved in the 20th century and the provenance of many Blue John pieces can now be more readily identified.

These examples made by John Walker in the Blue John Depot. Note the translucence of the middle vase

The Blue John Craft Shop and the Blue John Cavern

A Castleton local called John Walker came from a family with a background of Castleton trades associated with mining and tourism. He lived in Cavendish House on the corner of Cross Street in Castleton, where he had his Blue John workshop. From 1884, the building was referred to as the Blue John Depot, connected with the Blue John Cavern. John Walker made many ornaments, including a Blue John font for Castleton Methodist Chapel.

Arthur E Ollerenshaw bought the depot on John Walker's death, naming it the Blue John Craft Shop. It continues to this day to be run by the Ollerenshaw family, along with the Blue John Cavern whose workshops have produced many beautiful ornaments over the years.

Crute father and son

Fred Crute and his son Berkley were highly skilled stone craftsmen employed by Harry Grant & Sons until the 1970s when they set up their own works, Devon Art Stoneware. They produced many items in the 1970s and 1980s until they retired in the 1990s.

A selection of items made by Fred & Berkley Crute

Cyril Adamson

Cyril Adamson spent all his adult life mining and working with Blue John stone at Treak Cliff Cavern, producing mostly bowls and chalices and setting jewellery.

A fine pair of Millers Vein Obelisks made by Devon Art Stoneware

A goblet from Cyril Adamson

Blue John treasures of today

The Blue John Dragon

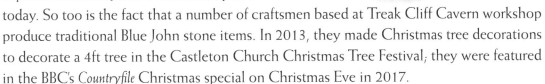

One of the greatest treasures at Treak Cliff Cavern is the Blue John Dragon. It was made in the workshop at the cavern by craftsman Peter Sharp over several months and was completed in 2014. Hand carved from Treak Cliff Blue Vein, with marcasite eyes, calcite spines, and sitting on a nest of quartz crystals, it is proof that Blue John craftsmanship is alive and well today. So too is the fact that a number of craftsmen based at Treak Cliff Cavern workshop produce traditional Blue John stone items. In 2013, they made Christmas tree decorations to decorate a 4ft tree in the Castleton Church Christmas Tree Festival; they were featured in the BBC's *Countryfile* Christmas special on Christmas Eve in 2017.

The Ridley Chalice

The Ridley Chalice was commissioned by Buxton Museum and Art Gallery for their new Millennium Galleries project in 2015. Craftsman Jack Mosley turned the chalice at Treak Cliff Cavern. It is made from Blue John that was mined by Gary Ridley, who discovered the first new distinctive vein for over 150 years.

The Blue John Window

This stunning internal window now has pride of place at Vernon Park Museum in Stockport. Crafted exquisitely from Blue John and measuring 6ft by 3ft, it was made by John Tym to fit an arched window in his house near Goosehill Bridge in Castleton. He made it over a period of five years in the 1870s in his workshop (now the Silver & Stone Shop) next door to his house using around 250 separate slices of Blue John stone, representing all the different patterns or veins. John Tym was curator of the Vernon Park Museum from 1885 until his death. While the site is no longer used as a museum the Blue John Window is still on display in the foyer.

The Chatsworth Blue John window

This window is made up of 81 pieces of Blue John, sadly it is not on general display.

The Blue John Window in Chatsworth

© Devonshire Collection, Chatsworth. Reproduced by permission of Chatsworth Settlement Trustees.

A new Blue John Window

Buxton Museum and Art Gallery commissioned a Blue John Window in 2015 for their Millennium Galleries. It was made at Treak Cliff Cavern and is a depiction of Castleton and the landscape viewed from the Cavern Visitor Centre.

Buxton Museum window

The 'Spirit' of Blue John

Caithness Glass have created three items inspired by Twelve Vein exclusively for Blue John Cavern. Each piece is unique and produced in limited editions.

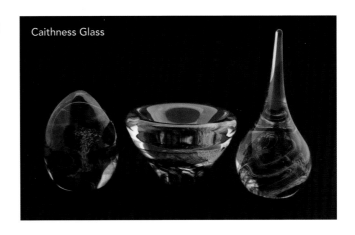
Caithness Glass

Modern jewellery

Blue John stone jewellery is widely available in Sterling Silver and 9ct Gold. There are several specialist Blue John shops in Castleton, with associated online shops. Further afield, for example in Bakewell, Buxton and Matlock, there are other Blue John craftspeople and retailers. But wherever it is made or sold, every item featuring Blue John stone will have originated from Treak Cliff Hill, Castleton in Derbyshire!

Blue John craftsman, Cyril Adamson (1929–2005) used to say, 'There's a customer for every piece'. How right he was. Given the incredible variety of patterns and colours of Blue John stone, there really is something crafted from this intriguing and eye catching mineral to suit every taste. With its rich history and unique beauty, there is no doubt that Blue John will continue to fascinate people for many centuries to come.

For details of other titles from Bradwell Books visit bradwellbooks.co.uk

NEW FOR 2018

Bradwell's Images of Derbyshire Well Dressing
ISBN 9781912060658

Bradwell's Histories - Bess of Hardwick
ISBN 9781912060627

Legends & Folklore the Peak District
ISBN 9781912060702

Walks for all Seasons Derbyshire
ISBN 9781912060528

AVAILABLE NOW

Derbyshire Dialect
ISBN 9781902674483

Derbyshire Ghost Stories
ISBN 9781902674629

Derbyshire Murder Stories
ISBN 9781909914285

Derbyshire Recipes
ISBN 9781902674858

Derbyshire Wit & Humour
ISBN 9781909914513

Bradwell's Family Cycle Rides: The Peak District
ISBN 9781910551868

Bradwell's Images of the Peak District
ISBN 9781909914759

Bradwell's Longer Walks in the Peak District
ISBN 9781910551677

Bradwell's Pocket Walking Guides the Peak District
ISBN 9781910551936

Bradwells Book of The Peak District
ISBN 9781912060573

Colour the Peak District
ISBN 9781912060740

Walks for All Ages Peak District
ISBN 9781909914018

Available from your local bookshop or order online bradwellbooks.co.uk